WISE PUBLICATIONS

LONDON/NEW YORK/SYDNEY

Exclusive Distributors: Music Sales Limited
8/9 Frith Street,
London W1V 5TZ, England.
Music Sales Pty Limited
120 Rothschild Avenue,
Rosebery, NSW 2018,
Australia.

This book © Copyright 1991 by Wise Publications
Order No. AM84468
ISBN 0.7119.2618.2

Design by Pearce Marchbank Studio
Compiled by Peter Evans

Music Sales' complete catalogue lists thousands of titles and is free
from your local music shop, or direct from Music Sales Limited.
Please send a cheque/postal order for £1.50 for postage to:
Music Sales Limited, Newmarket Road, Bury St. Edmunds, Suffolk IP33 3YB.

Your Guarantee of Quality

As publishers, we strive to produce every book to the highest commercial standards.
The book has been carefully designed to minimise awkward page
turns and to make playing from it a real pleasure.
Particular care has been given to specifying acid-free,
neutral-sized paper which has not been chlorine bleached but produced
with special regard for the environment. Throughout, the printing
and binding have been planned to ensure a sturdy,
attractive publication which should give years of enjoyment.
If your copy fails to meet our high standards, please inform
us and we will gladly replace it.

Printed in the United Kingdom by
Caligraving Limited, Thetford, Norfolk.

A WOMAN IN LOVE

WORDS & MUSIC BY BARRY GIBB & ROBIN GIBB

Moderately Slow

Life is a mo-ment in space,___ when the dream is gone___ it's a lone-li-er place.___
With you e-ter-nal-ly mine,___ in love there is___ no meas-ure of time.___

and hold you with-in _____ It's a right _____ I de - fend o - ver and o - ver a-

gain. What do I do?

To Coda ⊕

D.S. al Coda

CODA ⊕

What do I do?

I am a Wom - an In Love ___ and I'm talk - ing to you. ___ I know how you feel, ___

8

what a wom-an can do._____ It's a right_____ I de-fend

o - ver and o - ver a-gain._____ I am a Wom-an In Love,__

_____ and I'd do an - y - thing_____ to get you in - to my world,_____ and hold you with - in.__

Repeat and Fade

_____ It's a right_____ I de-fend   o - ver and o - ver a - gain.

The Way We Were

Music by Marvin Hamlisch. Words by Alan & Marilyn Bergman

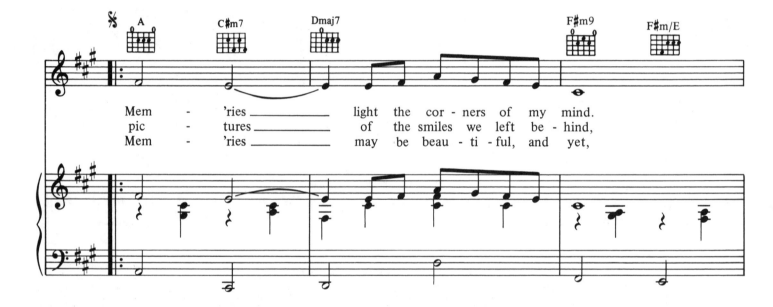

Mem - 'ries _____ light the cor - ners of my mind.
pic - tures _____ of the smiles we left be - hind,
Mem - 'ries _____ may be beau - ti - ful, and yet,

Mist - y wa - ter col - or mem - 'ries _____ of the way we
smiles we gave to one an - oth - er _____ for the way we
what's too pain - ful to re - mem - ber

were.   Scat - tered were. _____

Can it be that it was all so sim - ple then,   or has time re - writ - ten ev - 'ry line?

D.%. al Coda

If we had the chance to do it all a - gain, tell me would we?__ Could we?__

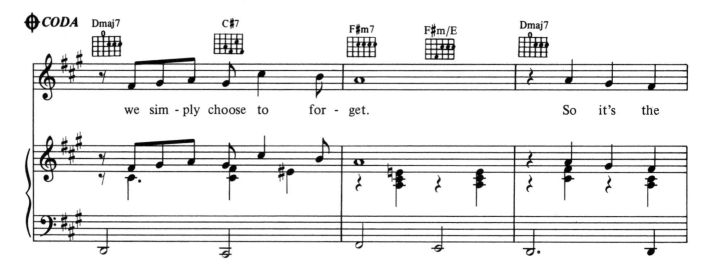

we sim - ply choose to for - get. So it's the

laugh - ter we will re - mem - ber,

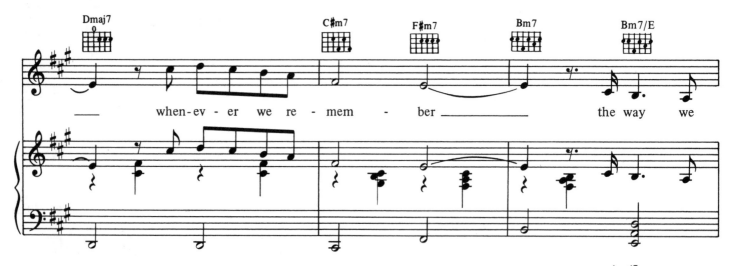

when-ev - er we re - mem - ber the way we

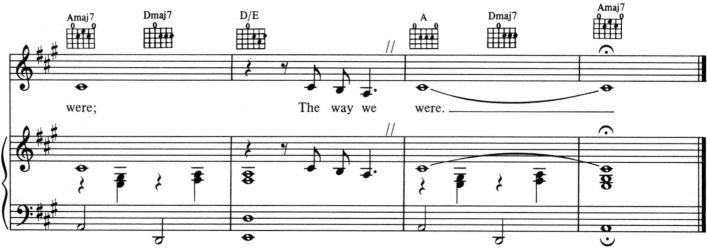

were; The way we were.

Somewhere

Music by Leonard Bernstein. Lyrics by Stephen Sondheim

15

CAN'T HELP LOVIN' DAT MAN

MUSIC BY JEROME KERN. WORDS BY OSCAR HAMMERSTEIN II

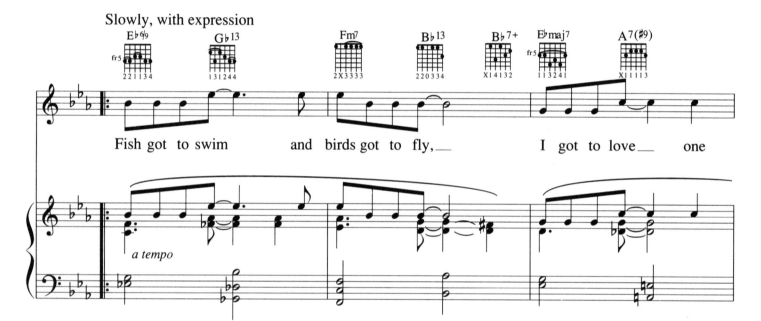

Fish got to swim and birds got to fly, __ I got to love __ one

man till I die, __ Can't help lov - in' dat man __ of

mine.   Tell me he's la - zy,

tell me he's slow,_   tell me I'm cra - zy,   may-be I know,_

Can't   help   lov-in' dat man_ of   mine.

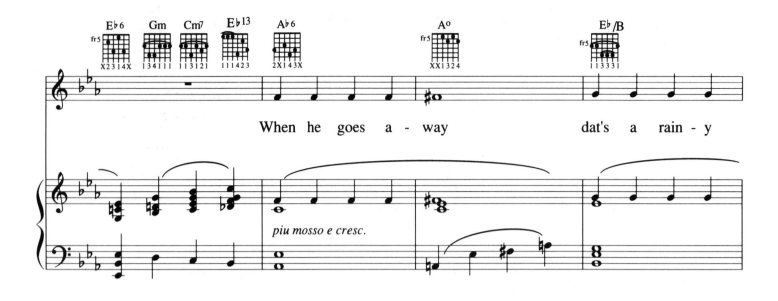

When he goes a - way dat's a rain - y

piu mosso e cresc.

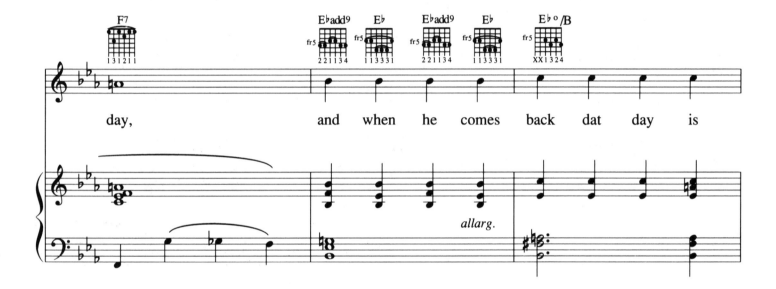

day, and when he comes back dat day is

allarg.

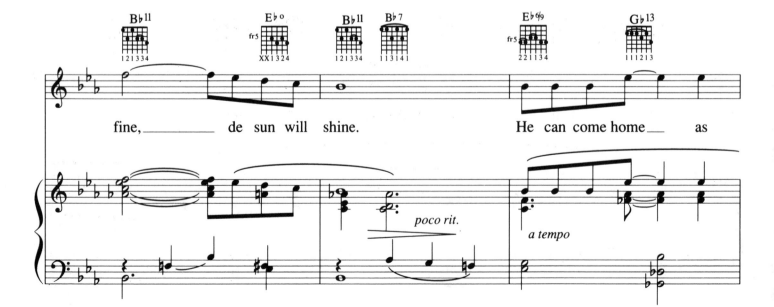

fine,_____ de sun will shine. He can come home___ as

poco rit.

a tempo

Send In The Clowns

Words & Music by Stephen Sondheim

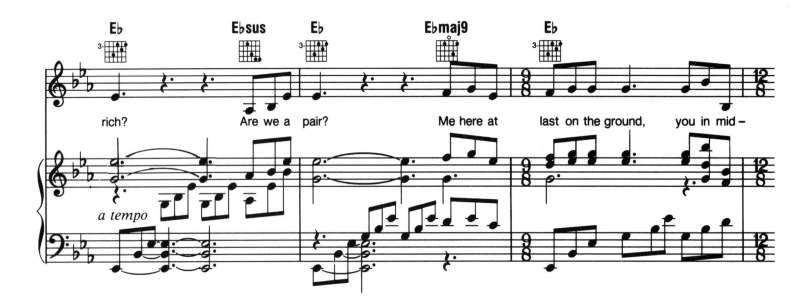

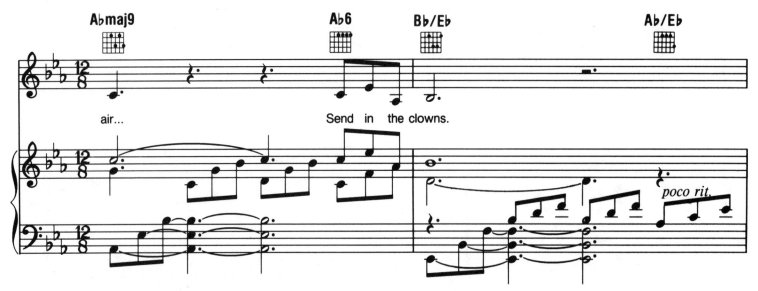

This arrangement includes Mr. Sondheim's revised lyrics for Barbra Streisand's recording.

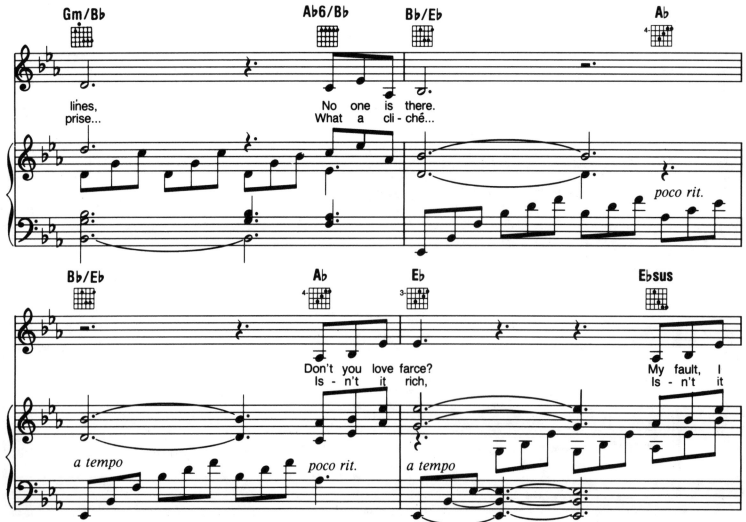

22

People

MUSIC BY JULIE STYNE. WORDS BY BOB MERRILL

Moderately

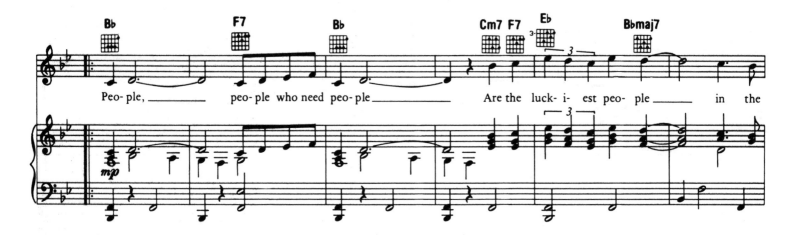

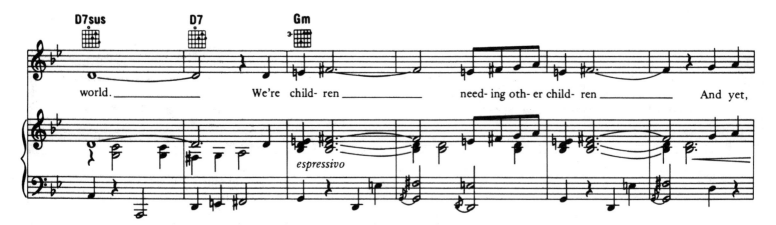

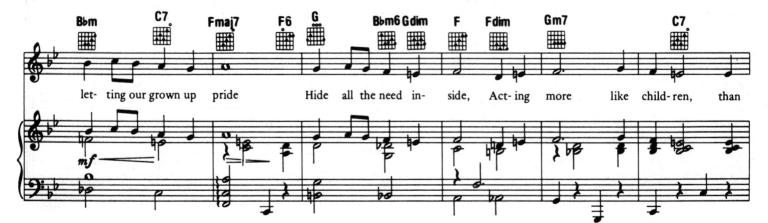

A Taste Of Honey

Words by Ric Marlow. Music by Bobby Scott

Rather Slow

Lyrics:

Winds may blow o'er the ic - y sea, I'll take with me the warmth of thee, A Taste of Hon - ey, A taste much sweet - er than

leave be - hind my heart to wear And may it e'er re - mind you of A Taste of Hon - ey, A taste much sweet - er than

ne'er came back to his love so fair And so she died dream - ing of his kiss. His kiss was Hon - ey, A taste much sweet - er than

Memory

Music by Andrew Lloyd Webber. Text by Trevor Nunn after T.S. Eliot

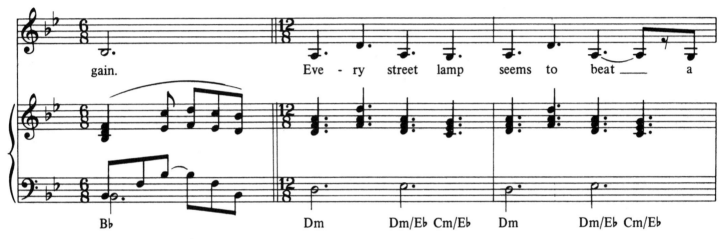

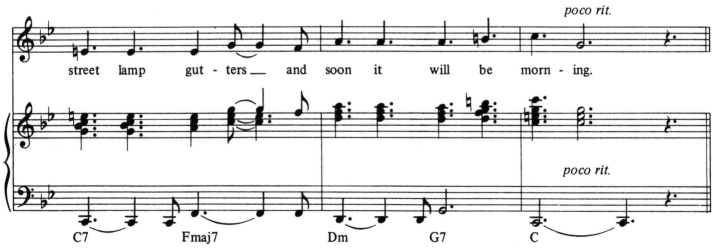

Day - light. _ I must wait for the sun - rise, _ I must think of a new life _ And I must-n't give

in. _ When the dawn comes to-night will be a mem-or-y too_ And a

new day _ will be - gin.

Instrumental

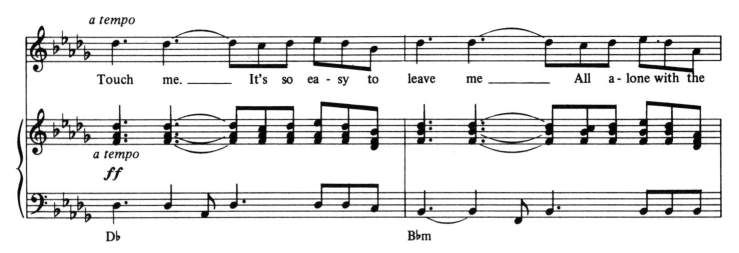

Touch me. _____ It's so ea - sy to leave me _____ All a - lone with the

Db   Bbm

mem - ory _____ Of my days in the sun. _____ If you touch me you'll un - der-stand what

Gb   Fm   Ebmsus   Ebm

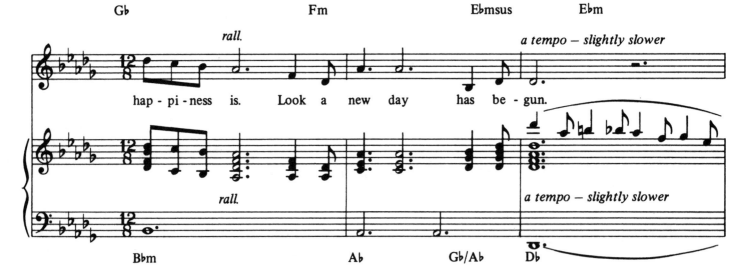

hap - pi - ness is. Look a new day has be - gun.

Bbm   Ab   Gb/Ab   Db

Stoney End

Words & Music by Laura Nyro

don't be - lieve I want to see __ the morn - ing!
don't be - lieve I want to see __ the

morn - ing!

Go - ing down the Ston - ey End, __

__ I nev - er want - ed to go __ down the Ston - ey End. __

Ma - ma let me start all o - ver. Cra - dle me, __ ma - ma, cra - dle me __

SOMETHING'S COMING

MUSIC BY LEONARD BERNSTEIN. LYRICS BY STEPHEN SONDHEIM

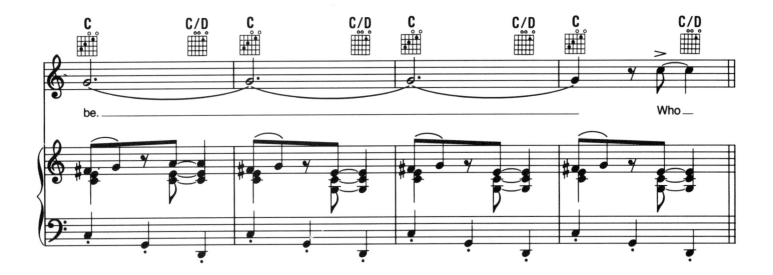

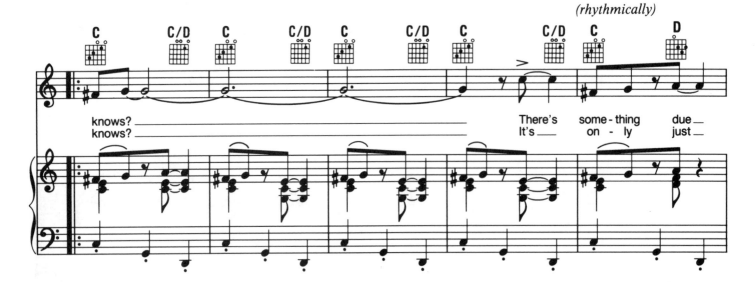

42

The air _____ is _____ hum - ming, _____ And some - thing _____ great _____ is com - ing. _____

44

New York State Of Mind

WORDS & MUSIC BY BILLY JOEL

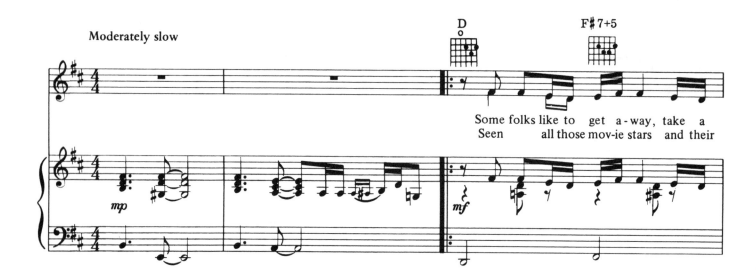

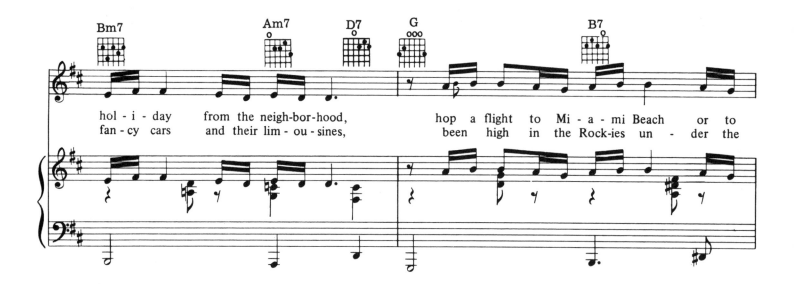

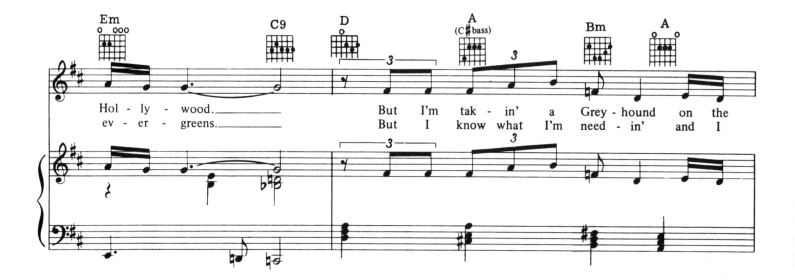

Hud - son Riv - er line,___ I'm in a New York state of
don't wan - na waste_ more time,___ I'm in a New York state of

mind.

mind.

It was so eas - y___ liv - in' day by day,_ out of touch_ with the rhy-thm and

blues. But now I need_ a lit - tle give and take,_ the

New York Times_ and the Dai-ly News._

Comes down to re-al-i-ty___ and it's fine with me_ 'cause I've let it slide,_____

I don't care_ if it's Chi-na-town_ or up on Riv-er-side._____

I don't have an-y rea-sons,___ I've left them all be-hind,

48

49

Evergreen

WORDS BY PAUL WILLIAMS. MUSIC BY BARBRA STREISAND

Moderately, with feeling

mp legato

with pedal throughout

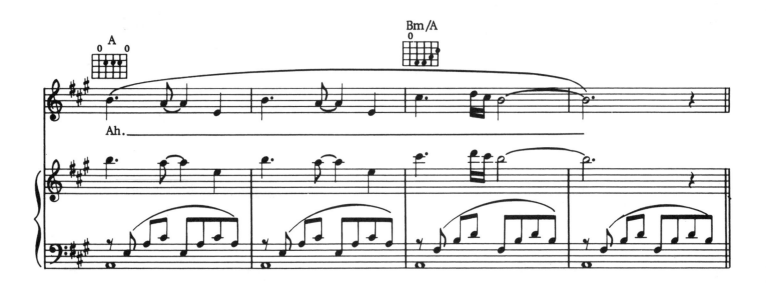

Ah._____

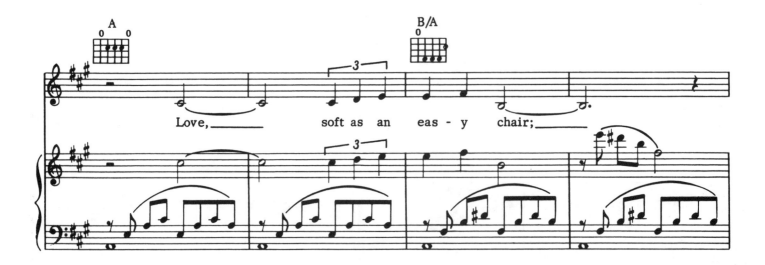

Love,_____ soft as an eas - y chair;_____

love, _____ fresh as the morn-ing air. _____

One _____ love that is shared by two, _____

I have found _____ with you. _____

_____ Like a rose _____ un-der the A - pril snow, _____

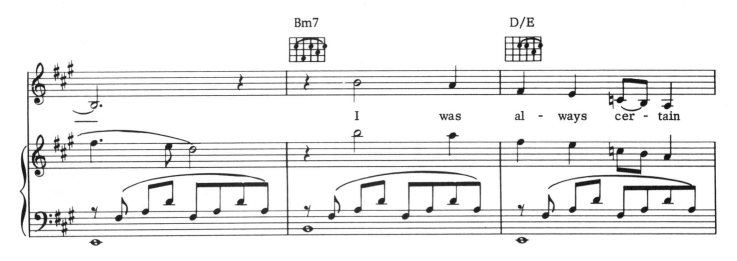

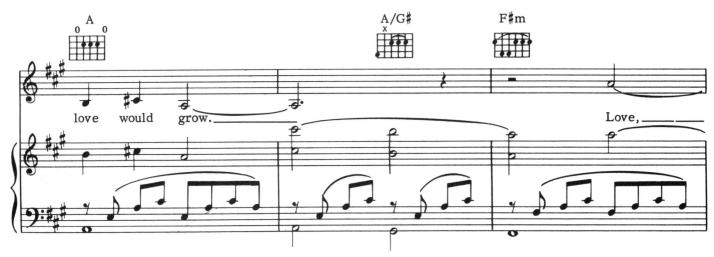

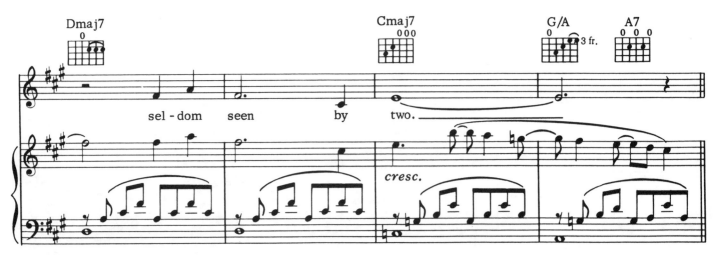

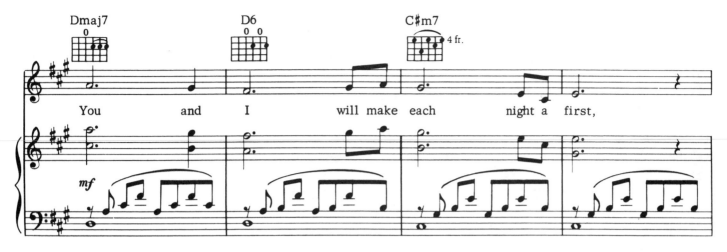

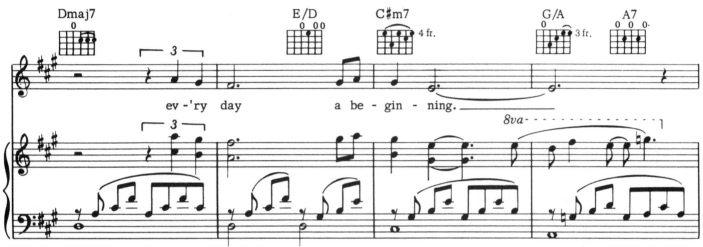

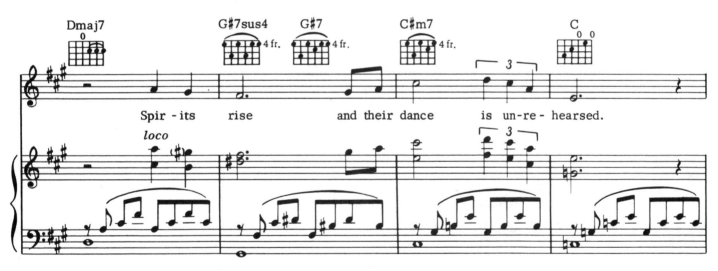

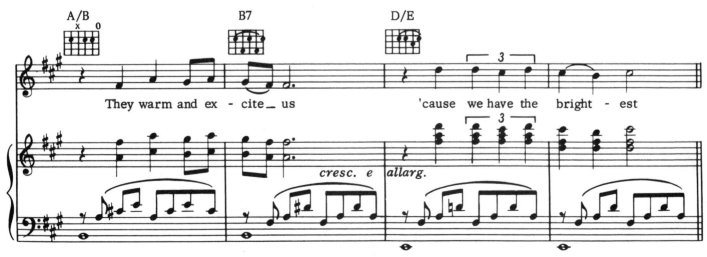

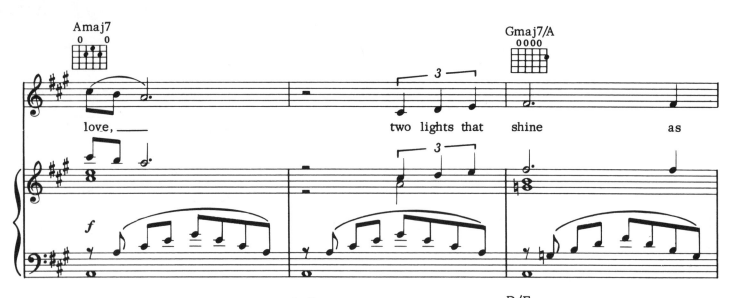

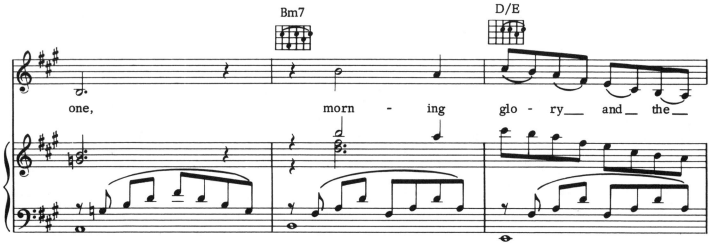

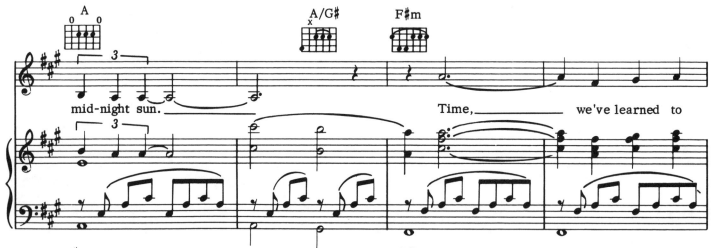

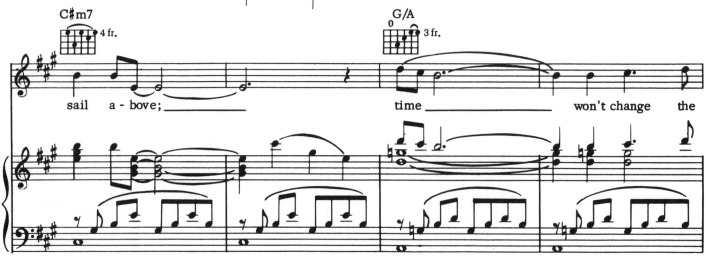

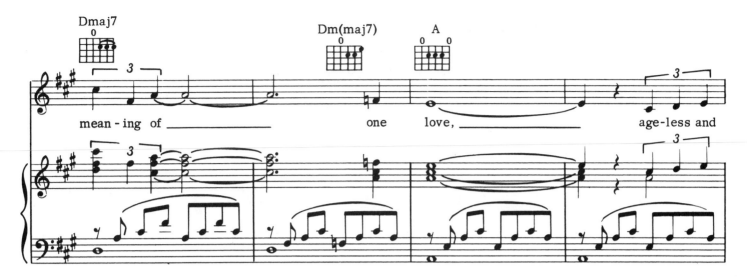

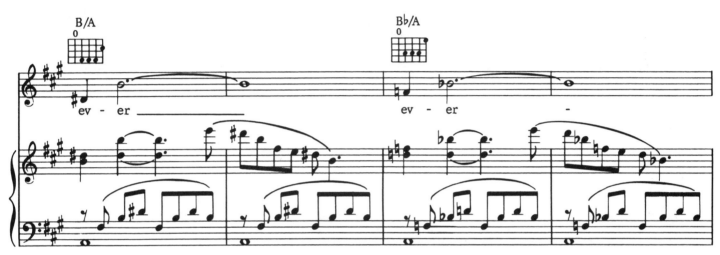

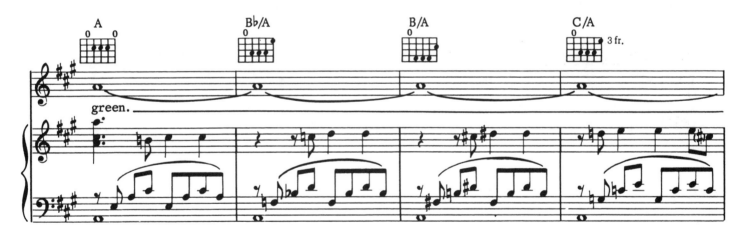

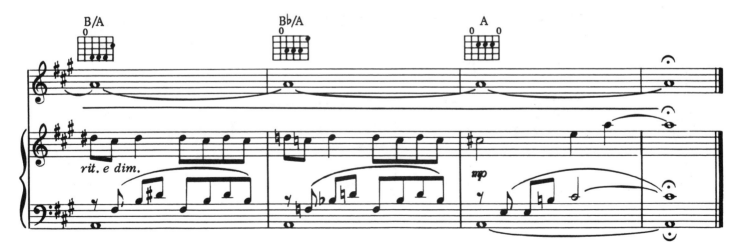

I Won't Last A Day Without You

Words by Paul Williams. Music by Roger Nichols

Day af-ter day___ I must
So man-y times___ when the

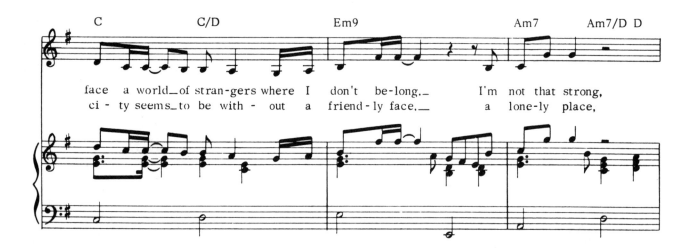

face a world__of stran-gers where I don't be-long.___ I'm not that strong,
ci-ty seems__to be with-out a friend-ly face.___ a lone-ly place,

it's nice to know___ that there's some-one I___ can turn to who will
it's nice to know___ that you'll be there if___ I need you and you'll

al-ways care, you're al-ways there,
al-ways smile, it's all worth while,
When there's no get-ting ov-er that

rain - bow, when my small - est of dreams won't come ____ true. I can

take all the mad - ness the world ____ has to give, ____ but I

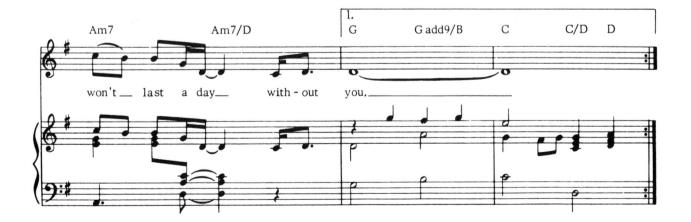

won't ____ last a day ____ with - out you. _____

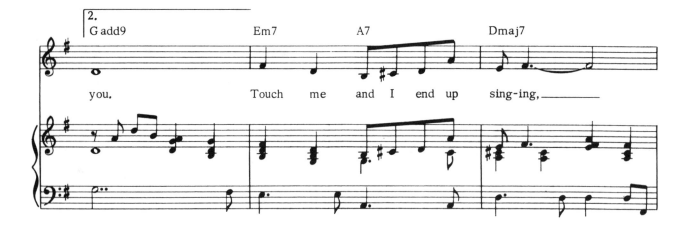

you. Touch me and I end up sing-ing, _____

trou-bles seem to up and dis-ap-pear, you touch me with the love you're

bring-ing, _____ I can't real-ly lose when you're near, When you're

near my _____ love, if all my friends _____ have for -

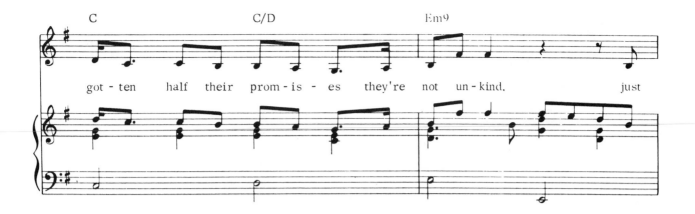

got - ten half their prom - is - es they're not un - kind, just

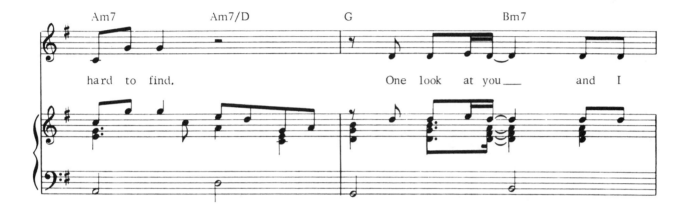

hard to find. One look at you___ and I

know that I___ could learn to live with - out the rest, I

found the best, When there's no get-ting ov-er that rain - bow When my

small - est of dreams__won't come__ true, I can

take all the mad - ness the world has to give, __ but I

won't last a day__ with-out. When There's Won't last a day___

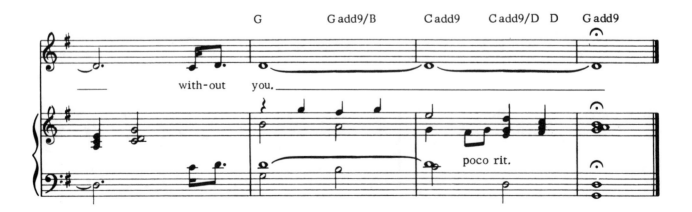

__ with-out you._____

poco rit.

GUILTY

WORDS & MUSIC BY BARRY GIBB, ROBIN GIBB & MAURICE GIBB

Moderately

Shad - ows fall - ing ba - by We stand a lone.

Out on the street_ an-y bo - dy you meet_ got a heart - ache of their own.

Make it a crime to be lone-ly or sad

You got a rea-son for liv - ing you bat - tle on with the

love you're liv - in' on you got-ta be mine. We take it a - way

It's got-ta be night and day just a mat-ter of time. And we got noth-ing to be

63

You got a rea-son for liv-in' you bat — tle — on with the love —

— you're build-in' on — you got-ta be mine._____ We take it a way.

D.S. al Coda

It's got-ta be night — and day just a mat-ter of time.— And we got noth-ing to be

CODA   Repeat and Fade

bye._____   Don't wan-na hear___ your _____ good

What Now My Love

ENGLISH WORDS BY CARL SIGMAN. FRENCH LYRIC BY PIERRE DELANOE. MUSIC BY GILBERT BECAUD

Moderate Bolero Tempo

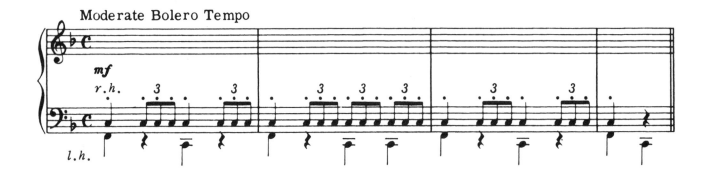

What Now My Love _____ Now that you left me _____ How can I
Love _____ Now that it's o - ver _____ I feel the

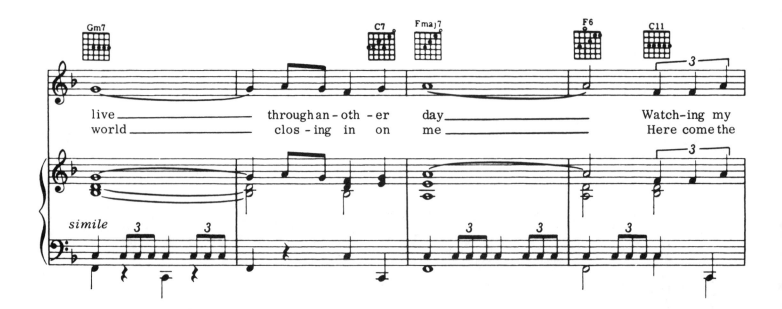

live _____ through an - oth - er day _____ Watch-ing my
world _____ clos - ing in on me _____ Here come the

dreams _____ Turn-ing to ash - es _____ And my
stars _____ Tum-bling a - round me _____ There's the

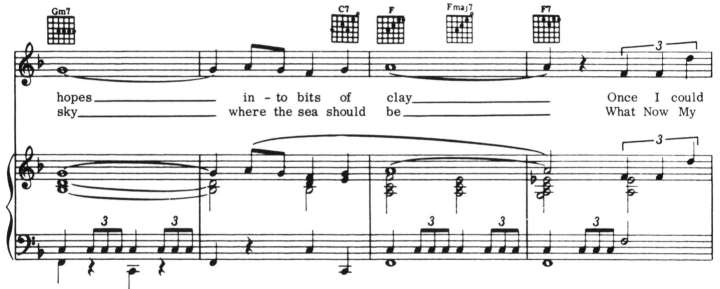

hopes _____ in - to bits of clay _____ Once I could
sky _____ where the sea should be _____ What Now My

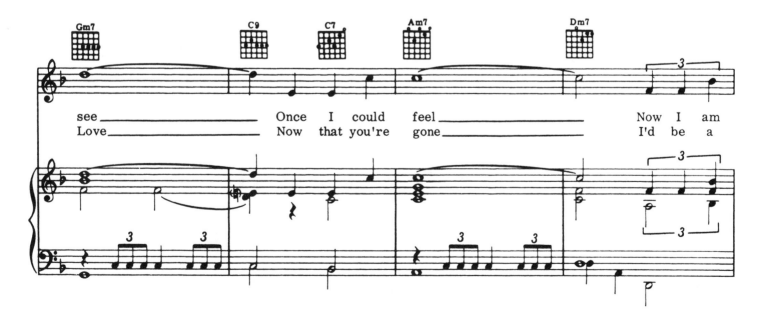

see _____ Once I could feel _____ Now I am
Love _____ Now that you're gone _____ I'd be a

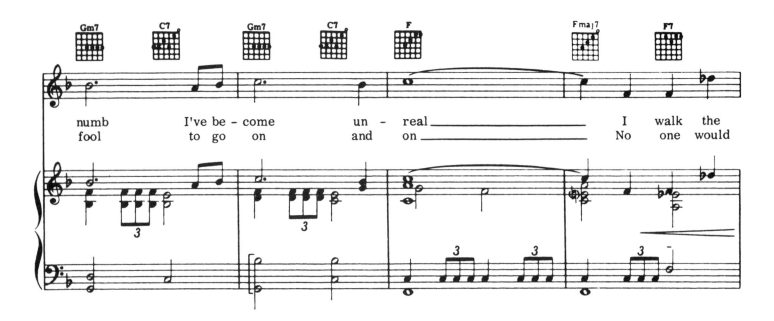

numb I've be - come un - real _____ I walk the
fool to go on and on _____ No one would

night _____ With - out a goal _____ Stripped of my
care _____ No one would cry _____ If I should

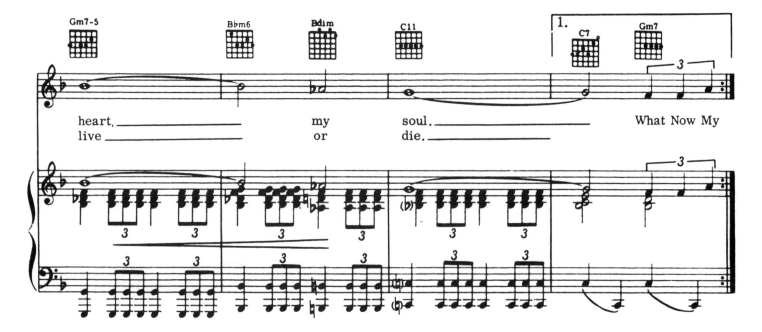

heart, _____ my soul. _____ What Now My
live _____ or die. _____ If I should

What Now My Love _____ Now there is

noth - ing _____ On - ly my last _____ good -

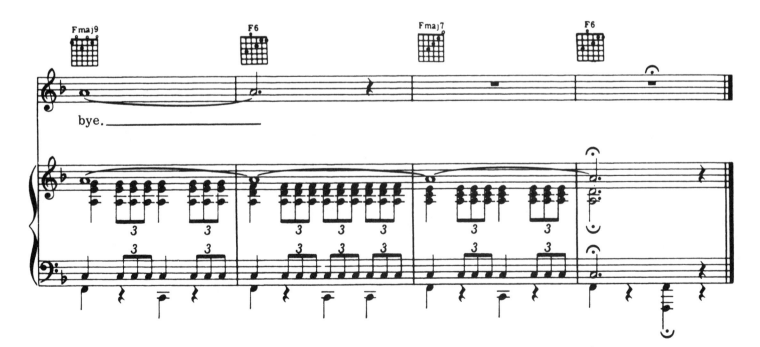

bye. _____

My Heart Belongs To Me

Words & Music by Alan Gordon

What Kind Of Fool Am I

Words & Music by Leslie Bricusse & Anthony Newley

Moderately slow

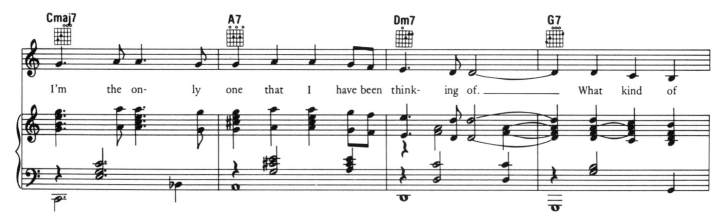

What kind of fool am I? Who nev-er fell in love, It seems that

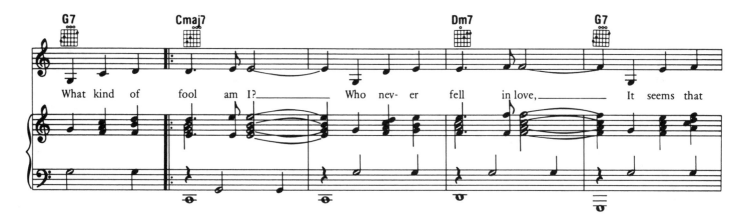

I'm the on-ly one that I have been think-ing of. What kind of

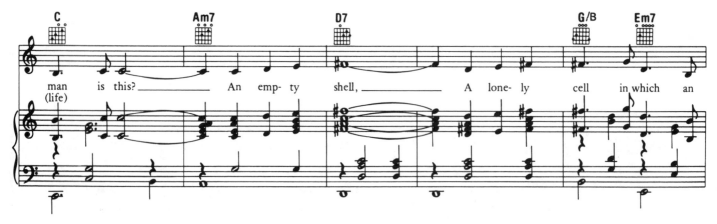

man is this? An emp-ty shell, A lone-ly cell in which an
(life)

You Don't Bring Me Flowers

Words by Neil Diamond, Marilyn Bergman & Alan Bergman.
Music by Neil Diamond

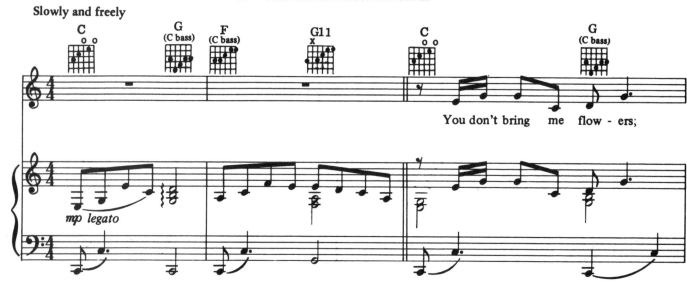

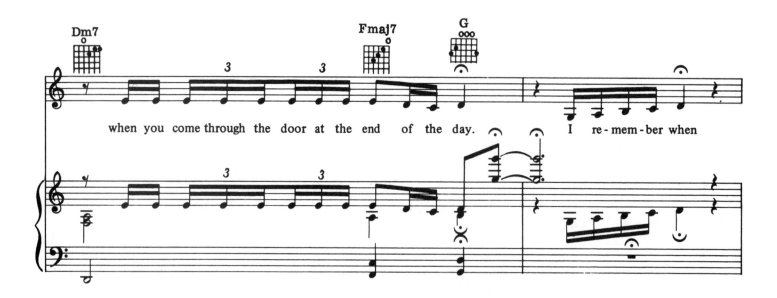

and you don't bring me flow-ers an-y-more.

It used to be so nat-'ral to talk a-bout for-ev-er,

but used-to-be's don't count an-y-more.__ They just lay on the floor till we sweep them a-way.

And ba-by, I re-mem-ber all the things you taught me:

a tempo

gradual cresc.